£3·75

GRADE

3

The Syllabus of Examinations should be read for details of requirements, especially those for scales, aural tests and sight-reading. Attention should be paid to the Special Notices on the inside front cover, where warning is given of any changes.

The syllabus is obtainable from music retailers or from The Associated Board of the Royal Schools of Music, 24 Portland Place, London W1B 1LU (please send a stamped addressed C5 (162mm x 229mm) envelope).

In examination centres outside the UK, information and syllabuses may be obtained from the Local Representative.

CONTENTS

Where appropriate, pieces in this volume have been checked with original source material and edited as necessary for instructional purposes. Fingering, phrasing, pedalling, metronome marks and the editorial realization of ornaments (where given) are for guidance but are not comprehensive or obligatory.

Editor for the Associated Board: **Richard Jones**

DO NOT PHOTOCOPY © MUSIC

Alternative pieces for this grade

Music origination by Barnes Music Engraving Ltd.
Cover by Økvik Design.
Printed in England by Headley Brothers Ltd,
The Invicta Press, Ashford, Kent.

Fantasia in D minor

H. 224, Wq. 117/12

Edited by
Howard Ferguson

C. P. E. BACH

Allegro di molto [♩ = *c*.104]

Carl Philipp Emanuel (1714–88), Bach's second eldest son, served as harpsichordist to Frederick the Great in Berlin for nearly 30 years. In 1767 he succeeded Telemann as Cantor and Music Director at Hamburg. In this piece the dynamics are editorial suggestions only.

Saraband in C

A:2

BLOW

John Blow (1649–1708) was a Gentleman of the Chapel Royal from 1674 and Organist of Westminster Abbey from 1668. He relinquished this post in 1679 to make way for his brilliant young pupil Henry Purcell, but was reinstated after Purcell's death in 1695. Dotted-crotchet rhythms would have been double-dotted, and undotted crotchets might be lightly detached. Quaver pairs are notated equally in the source (except in bar 15) but Blow's later, more elaborate version shows that they would have been played unequally as printed here. Only the slurs of bar 3 are original; all other slurs and the dynamics are editorial suggestions only. Of the original ornamentation only the trills at cadences (indicated by the sign ⌇ in the source) have been retained here.

Source: *The Second Part of Musick's Hand-maid* (London, 1689)

Selected from *Baroque Keyboard Pieces*, Book I, edited by Richard Jones (Associated Board)

L'Agréable

DANDRIEU

Jean-François Dandrieu (*c.*1682–1738), organist at the royal chapel in Paris from 1721, was, after Couperin and Rameau, the most celebrated French harpsichord composer of the early 18th century. *L'Agréable* is a gavotte, a pastoral type of French dance in moderate duple time. It is likely that slurred quavers would have been played with an unequal lilt (♩♩ = ♩³♪), unmarked quavers evenly. Unslurred crotchets might be lightly detached. All slurs and dynamics are editorial suggestions only.
Source: [1*er*] *Livre de pièces de clavecin* (Paris, 1724).

Selected from *Baroque Keyboard Pieces*, Book I, edited by Richard Jones (Associated Board)

Proud Horseman

No. 2 from *Jugend-Album*, Op. 47

B:1

Edited by
Alan Jones

R. FUCHS

The *Children's Album* (*Jugend-Album*), Op. 47, by the Austrian composer Robert Fuchs (1847–1927) is one of the many 19th-century collections of piano pieces that belong to the tradition of Schumann's *Album for the Young*.

AB 2735

Mazurka in C

B:2

Edited by
Lionel Salter

GLINKA

Mikhail Ivanovich Glinka (1804–57), who was taught the piano by John Field at St Petersburg, is regarded as the founder of the Russian nationalist school of composers.

Poco lento

No. 7 from *Stücke für Enkel*

B:3

T. F. KIRCHNER

Edited by
Chris Walton

Theodor Kirchner (1823–1903) was a pupil of Mendelssohn and an acquaintance of Schumann and Brahms. His *Pieces for Grandchildren* (*Stücke für Enkel*) of 1881 were published in the following year as piano trios, the 15 *Children's Trios*, Op. 58.

Playing Ball

No. 5 from *30 Pieces for Children*, Op. 27

KABALEVSKY

C:2

Safe Landing

No. 3 from *Stevie's Ferry to Hoy*

PETER MAXWELL DAVIES

All dynamics other than those of the first bar are editorial suggestions only.

Melancholy

from *Little Stories in Jazz*

MIKE SCHOENMEHL

C:3

The composer tells us that the accompaniment should be considerably quieter than the melody. He also says that players with large hands might consider playing the lower-stave crotchets in bars 1–2 and the like with the right thumb.